WeightWatchers®

vegetarian
cooking

Jo Middleditch

SIMON & SCHUSTER
A VIACOM COMPANY

First published in Great Britain by Simon & Schuster, 1997
A Viacom Company

This edition produced for
The Book People Ltd
Hall Wood Avenue
Haydock
St Helens
WA11 9UL

Copyright © 1997, Weight Watchers International, Inc.

First published 1997
Reprinted 2002

Simon & Schuster UK Ltd
Africa House
64–78 Kingsway
London WC2B 6AH

This book is copyright under the Berne Convention
No reproduction without permission
All rights reserved

Weight Watchers and 1,2,3 Success are Trademarks of Weight Watchers
International Inc. and used under its control by Weight Watchers (U.K.) Ltd

Design: Moore Lowenhoff
Cover design: Zoocity
Typesetting: Stylize
Photography: Edward Allwright
Styling: Kay McGlone
Food preparation: Berit Vinegrad

ISBN 0-68482-102-8

Printed in Hong Kong

Recipe notes:
Egg size is medium, unless otherwise stated.
Vegetables are medium-sized, unless otherwise stated.
It is very important to use proper measuring spoons, not cutlery, for spoon measures.
1 tablespoon = 15 ml; 1 teaspoon = 5 ml
Dried herbs can be substituted for fresh ones, but the flavour may not always
be as good. Halve the fresh-herb quantity stated in the recipe.

Contents

Introduction

Vegetarian eating has really taken off in the 90s; all sorts of people of different ages are now following a vegetarian diet or enjoying vegetarian meals. We've begun to understand that vegetarian food does not mean simply taking the meat out of a traditional meat-and-two-veg meal; it's a style of cooking in its own right – delicious, contemporary and exciting.

The thirty recipes in *Vegetarian Cooking* are simple to follow and can be put together with the minimum of fuss – and they taste wonderful too. But that's just as it should be: watching your weight should never leave you feeling deprived or hungry.

However vegetarian food can pose a few problems for those of us trying to shed a few pounds; there's a temptation to replace meat with high-fat cheese and other dairy products – which won't do our waistlines much good. In *Vegetarian Cooking* you'll find I've made good use of the other protein foods which are suitable for vegetarians: beans and pulses, nuts and seeds and grains. But there's no need to avoid dairy products altogether. Low-fat versions of dairy products can easily fit into the Weight Watchers Programme. Or add just a little well-flavoured mature cheese to a dish for a delicious tangy taste.

As a vegetarian you need to make sure that you are eating a varied diet. Any diet, whether vegetarian or not, that is limited to just a few foods risks missing out on one or more essential nutrients, but with a wide variety of foods any deficiency in one area is made up by something else.

A word or two about ingredients:

All cheeses (except those made from soya or similar vegetable products) are made from milk. Traditionally the milk is clotted with rennet from calves' stomachs and this has meant that, until recently, the range of cheeses for vegetarians has been rather limited. Now a clotting enzyme has been produced, by genetic modification, that is suitable for vegetarians; cheeses made in this way are commonly available (labelled 'suitable for vegetarians') and the range is growing all the time. We now have vegetarian Stilton, Cheddar and Cheshire. However vegetarian Parmesan can be a little difficult to find and so I have given an alternative wherever it is used.

Where a recipe includes Cheddar, the Points are based on low-fat vegetarian Cheddar. The table below shows how the Points change if you use a regular Cheddar.

	Points per 40g	Per tablespoon grated
Cheddar (vegetarian and non-vegetarian)	$4^1/_2$	1
low-fat Cheddar (vegetarian and non-vegetarian)	$2^1/_2$	$^1/_2$

Some supermarkets stock half-fat mozzarella. Consider using this to reduce your Points.

In some recipes I have used Quorn. Quorn is not approved by the Vegetarian Society as it contains egg white which is not guaranteed to be from free-range eggs. You can, if you wish, substitute tofu or soya mince.

I hope you find this book enjoyable and inspirational and that it becomes part of a well-thumbed collection of recipe books. Happy eating!

Salads and Stir-Fries

The salads in this chapter are substantial enough to be a meal in themselves – perfect for lunch or as a light meal. Do try the crunchy Vegetable Salad drizzled with a rich, hot peanut dressing, and the Mediterranean Salsa Salad which has a delicious garlic, herb, watercress and caper dressing.

Stir-fries are wonderful – and so versatile. They are full of exciting flavours and delicious, colourful vegetables, which are cooked only lightly so that they preserve their vitamins and crunchy texture. Very little oil is used so these dishes are also low in Points. This chapter has a mouth-watering range of stir-fries for you to try: Chinese, Mexican or Balti-style – it's your choice!

Mediterranean Salsa Salad

Serves: 4
Preparation and cooking time: 15 minutes
Calories per serving: 200
Points per serving: 5
Total Points per recipe: 20
Freezing: not recommended

1 small Iceberg lettuce or 3 Little Gem lettuces, chopped
2 carrots, cut into matchsticks
1 tablespoon capers
180 g (6 oz) feta cheese, cubed

For the dressing:
1 tablespoon olive oil
1/2 teaspoon balsamic or red wine vinegar
1 tablespoon lemon juice
1/2 tablespoon capers
30 g (1 oz) watercress
1 small garlic clove, crushed
1 tablespoon chopped fresh parsley
1 tablespoon snipped chives
For the croûtons:
2 teaspoons sunflower oil
1 slice white bread, crusts removed, and cut into cubes

1 Toss together the lettuce, carrots and capers. Arrange on 4 serving plates.

2 Place all the dressing ingredients in a food processor or blender, and blend until thoroughly combined.

3 For the croûtons: heat the oil in a small non-stick heavy-based frying-pan and fry the bread cubes tossing constantly until golden. Remove from the pan.

4 Place the feta cheese on top of the salad, pour over the dressing and add the croûtons. Serve immediately.

Vegetable Salad with Peanut Dressing

Rice noodles are a traditional ingredient in Thai stir-fry dishes, soups and salads. They are very simple to prepare since they only need to be soaked in boiling water for 5 minutes.

Serves: 4
Preparation and cooking time: 15 minutes
Calories per serving: 250
Points per serving: 6
Total Points per recipe: 24
Freezing: not recommended

For the salad:
45 g (1¹/₂ oz) rice noodles
120 g (4 oz) sugarsnap peas
12–14 Chinese leaves, shredded

2 carrots, sliced into long thin strips
120 g (4 oz) baby sweetcorn, halved lengthways
2 spring onions, chopped
1 large red pepper, de-seeded and cut into
  thin strips
60 g (2 oz) salted peanuts
For the dressing:
3 tablespoons crunchy unsweetened peanut butter
2 teaspoons chilli sauce
1 teaspoon soy sauce
150 ml (¹/₄ pint) water

❶ Place the noodles in a bowl and cover with boiling water. Leave them to soak for 5 minutes and then drain.

❷ Meanwhile, blanch the sugarsnap peas in boiling water for a few seconds. Tip into a colander and refresh under cold running water. Leave to drain.

❸ Mix together the remaining salad ingredients in a serving bowl.

❹ Place the dressing ingredients in a saucepan over a medium heat and stir until thoroughly combined and warmed through.

❺ Add the noodles and sugarsnap peas to the salad. Pour the warm dressing over the salad and toss to coat. Serve immediately.

Stir-Fried Egg Noodles

This noodle dish with omelette strips and chopped peanuts is deliciously gingery.

Serves: 1
Preparation and cooking time: 15–20 minutes
Calories per serving: 670
Points per serving: 8
Freezing: not recommended

60 g (2 oz) egg noodles
1¹/₂ teaspoons sunflower oil
1 free-range egg, beaten
1 shallot, chopped
1 small carrot, sliced
60 g (2 oz) sugarsnap peas
60 g (2 oz) baby sweetcorn, halved lengthways
¹/₂ red pepper, de-seeded and chopped

60 g (2 oz) closed-cup mushrooms, sliced
2 spring onions, chopped
30 g (1 oz) beansprouts
15 g (¹/₂ oz) salted peanuts or cashew nuts,
  chopped
¹/₂ teaspoon sesame seeds
salt and freshly ground black pepper
For the sauce:
2 tablespoons light soy sauce
¹/₂ tablespoon freshly grated root ginger
1 garlic clove, crushed
¹/₂ teaspoon sesame oil
a pinch of chilli powder

① Mix the sauce ingredients together in a small bowl.

② Cook the noodles in a large pan of boiling water according to the directions on the packet. Tip the noodles into a colander and refresh under cold running water. Leave to drain.

③ Meanwhile, heat ½ teaspoon of the oil in a wok. Beat the egg with some seasoning and pour into the wok to make a thin omelette. Cook until set and then flip over and cook until golden. Remove from the wok with a palette knife and allow to cool before cutting into thin strips.

④ Add the remaining teaspoon of oil to the pan and stir-fry the vegetables over a high heat for 2–3 minutes. Add the noodles, omelette strips and sauce and stir-fry for a minute until heated through. Add the peanuts (or cashew nuts) and sesame seeds. Toss together and serve immediately.

Cook's note: You can choose extra vegetables from the 0 Point list to add to your stir-fries without changing the Points of the recipe.

Balti-Style Stir-Fry

Balti is now very popular. In Pakistan, it is a traditional way of cooking curry. Vegetables are stir-fried with a mixture of spices and then left to simmer until tender. In this recipe, ready-made Balti paste is ideal for speed and convenience. To eat the traditional way, use naan breads to scoop up the curry.

Serves: 4
Preparation and cooking time: 20 minutes
Calories per serving: 240
Points per serving: 6½
Total Points per recipe: 26
Freezing: not recommended

1 tablespoon sunflower oil
1 teaspoon finely grated root ginger
1 small onion, chopped
2 garlic cloves, crushed

4 tablespoons Balti curry paste
240 g (8 oz) cauliflower florets, cut into smaller florets
120 g (4 oz) young spinach leaves, chopped finely
2 tomatoes, quartered
420 g (14 oz) canned chick-peas, rinsed and drained
240 ml (8 fl oz) water
2 tablespoons chopped fresh coriander leaves
4 mini naans, warmed according to packet directions, to serve

① Heat the oil in a wok and stir-fry the ginger, onion and garlic for 5 minutes or until golden. Add the curry paste and cauliflower and stir-fry for a further 5 minutes.

② Add the spinach, tomatoes, chick-peas and water. Simmer for 5–8 minutes. Stir in the coriander and serve immediately with the naan breads. Use the bread to scoop up the curry instead of a knife and fork.

Variation: You could use medium pitta breads instead of the naans. This will make the Points per serving 6.

Mexican Stir-Fry

This is a great dish to share with friends – it's so simple to make yet really scrumptious! The traditional way to serve the meal is to lay out the pancakes and the stir-fry separately and let everyone help themselves. Top your pancake with some stir-fry and yogurt, and then roll it up and eat it with your fingers – which means no cutlery to wash up. Perfect!

Serves: 4
Preparation and cooking time: 15–20 minutes
Calories per serving: 430
Points per serving: 6
Total Points per recipe: 24
Freezing: not recommended

1 tablespoon sunflower oil
1 red onion, quartered and sliced
2 garlic cloves, crushed
1 red pepper, de-seeded and chopped
1 yellow pepper, de-seeded and chopped
1 green pepper, de-seeded and chopped
1 teaspoon cayenne pepper
2 teaspoons cumin seeds
2 courgettes, chopped
3 tomatoes, chopped roughly
150 g (5 oz) baby sweetcorn, halved
2 tablespoons chopped fresh coriander leaves
salt and freshly ground black pepper
To serve:
8 soft wheatflour tortillas
150 ml (5 fl oz) Greek yogurt

1 Heat the oil in a frying-pan or wok and fry the onion, garlic and peppers for 3–4 minutes. Then add the cayenne and cumin and cook for 2 minutes. Add the courgettes, tomatoes and sweetcorn and cook for a further 5–7 minutes. Stir in the coriander and seasoning, and pile onto a large serving dish.

2 Wrap the tortillas in foil and heat in a moderate oven for 3–4 minutes.

3 To serve, spoon some of the stir-fry mixture onto a warmed tortilla and top with a spoonful of Greek yogurt. Roll up the pancake and eat with your fingers!

Vegetable Salad with Peanut Dressing
Mexican Stir-Fry

Sweet and Sour Quorn

This stir-fry is full of wonderful flavours. Use Sharwoods Plum Sauce to ensure your dish has the best flavour – it is amazing how much different brands vary. This dish uses Quorn pieces which are fried in a little sesame oil for added flavour.

Serves: 4
Preparation and cooking time: 25–30 minutes
Calories per serving: 445
Points per serving: 8
Total Points per recipe: 32
Freezing: not recommended

2 teaspoons sunflower oil
$^1/_2$ teaspoon sesame oil
240 g (8 oz) Quorn pieces
1 garlic clove, crushed
5 cm (2–inch) root ginger, grated
2 carrots, cut into matchsticks
1 large courgette, cut into matchsticks
1 red pepper, de-seeded and chopped
90 g (3 oz) mange-tout peas

4 large spring onions, chopped finely
225 g (7$^1/_2$ oz) canned water chestnuts, rinsed
   and drained
240 g (8 oz) long-grain rice, cooked, to serve
For the sauce:
1 teaspoon arrowroot
120 ml (4 fl oz) water
3 tablespoons Sharwoods Plum Sauce
2 tablespoons white wine vinegar
2 tablespoons freshly squeezed pineapple juice
1 tablespoon light soy sauce
1 tablespoon medium dry sherry
1 tablespoon clear honey
2 tablespoons soft light brown sugar
1 teaspoon tomato purée

❶ Heat 1 teaspoon of the sunflower oil with the sesame oil in a wok. Stir-fry the Quorn for a few minutes until golden. Remove from the wok with a slotted spoon and set aside.

❷ Prepare the sauce. Dissolve the arrowroot in a little of the water in a small saucepan. Add the remaining water and sauce ingredients. Slowly bring to the boil, stirring often and then simmer for a couple of minutes. Remove from the heat and set aside.

❸ Add the remaining oil to the wok and stir-fry the garlic, ginger, carrots, courgette and pepper, over a high heat for 3–4 minutes. Then add the mange-tout peas, spring onions, and water chestnuts. Stir-fry for 1 or 2 minutes.

❹ Add the Quorn and the sauce to the wok and cook for a further minute or until piping hot. Serve immediately on a bed of cooked rice.

Pasta and Rice

Pasta and rice are staple foods all over the world and are the perfect base for quick and tasty vegetarian meals. High in complex carbohydrates and low in fat, they're easy on your waistline, *and* on your cheque book.

This chapter shows just how versatile they can be. Not only are they ideal convenience foods since they are so easy to prepare, but they also go wonderfully well with a wide variety of spices and ingredients. You'll love these exciting dishes which have been inspired by the flavouring, spices and culinary techniques of many regions around the world.

Spicy Pilaf

Coriander-flavoured yogurt is delicious with this spicy rice dish – try fresh mint too for a refreshing change along with some chopped or grated cucumber.

Serves: 4
Preparation and cooking time: 35 minutes
Calories per serving: 500
Points per serving: 7¹/₂
Total Points per recipe: 30
Freezing: not recommended

2 tablespoons sunflower oil
1 onion, chopped
2 garlic cloves, crushed
2 teaspoons freshly grated root ginger

1 carrot, chopped
1 small aubergine, chopped
3 tablespoons mild curry paste
240 g (8 oz) white basmati rice
750 ml (1¹/₄ pints) vegetable stock
60 g (2 oz) raisins
60 g (2 oz) flaked almonds, toasted
1 tablespoon chopped fresh coriander
To serve:
300 ml (¹/₂ pint) natural bio-yogurt
2 tablespoons chopped fresh coriander

❶ Heat the oil in a heavy-based saucepan and fry the onion over a high heat for 2 minutes until golden. Reduce the heat, add the garlic, ginger, carrot and aubergine and fry over a moderate heat, stirring frequently, for 5 minutes. Then stir in the curry paste and rice and cook, stirring for a further minute.

❷ Pour in the stock and stir in the raisins. Bring the pan to the boil. Reduce the heat until it simmers gently, then cover and cook for 15 minutes.

❸ Meanwhile, mix the yogurt with the chopped coriander.

❹ Remove the rice from the heat without removing the lid and leave to stand for 3 minutes, then fluff up with a fork and mix in the almonds and coriander. Serve immediately topped with the yogurt mixture.

Tomato and Aubergine Lasagne

Using low-fat cheese in this recipe makes it a tasty and slimming treat.

Serves: 4

Preparation time: 45 minutes + 40 minutes cooking

Calories per serving: 430

Points per serving: 5

Total Points per recipe: 20

Freezing: recommended

2 aubergines, sliced into 0.5 cm (¹/₄-inch) slices
1 tablespoon olive oil
360 g (12 oz) closed-cup or chestnut mushrooms, sliced
salt and freshly ground black pepper

120 g (4 oz) pre-cooked wholewheat lasagne sheets
90 g (3 oz) vegetarian mozzarella cheese, sliced
For the tomato sauce:
1 onion, chopped
2 garlic cloves, chopped
2 × 420 g (14 oz) canned plum tomatoes
3 tablespoons tomato purée
For the cheese sauce:
4 tablespoons cornflour
600 ml (1 pint) skimmed milk
60 g (2 oz) low-fat mature vegetarian Cheddar cheese, grated
1 teaspoon English mustard

❶ Preheat the oven to Gas Mark 6/200°C/400°F.

❷ Place the aubergine slices on two greased baking sheets. Bake in the oven for 15–20 minutes or until golden.

❸ Heat ¹/₂ tablespoon of the oil in a non-stick frying-pan. Add the mushrooms and seasoning, and fry for 5–8 minutes until golden and tender. Remove from the heat and set aside.

❹ For the tomato sauce: heat the remaining ¹/₂ tablespoon of oil in a saucepan and fry the onion for 10 minutes. Add the garlic and cook for another 2 minutes. Add the tomatoes, tomato purée and seasoning and simmer for 10 minutes.

❺ For the cheese sauce: mix the cornflour with a little of the milk in a saucepan and then beat in the remaining milk. Cook over a moderate heat, stirring frequently until thickened. Stir in the cheese and mustard, season to taste and remove the pan from the heat and set aside.

❻ To assemble the dish, put half of the mushrooms in the base of a large shallow oven-proof baking dish. Cover with one third of the tomato sauce, half the lasagne sheets, half the cheese sauce and half the aubergine slices. Repeat the layers and finish with the remaining tomato sauce. Arrange the mozzarella cheese on top.

❼ Bake in the preheated oven for 30–40 minutes until golden and bubbling.

Tomato and Aubergine Lasagne
Middle Eastern-Style Peppers

Spanish Tomato Rice

The combination of rice and black-eyed beans makes this a very nutritious dish.

Serves: 4
Preparation and cooking time: 30 minutes
Calories per serving: 380
Points per serving: 6¹/₂
Total Points per recipe: 26
Freezing: not recommended

1 tablespoon olive oil
1 onion, chopped
2 garlic cloves, crushed
1 red pepper, de-seeded and chopped
1 courgette, chopped
1 teaspoon chilli powder

1 teaspoon turmeric
240 g (8 oz) long-grain rice
450 ml (³/₄ pint) vegetable stock
4 tablespoons dry white wine
420 g (14 oz) canned chopped tomatoes
180 g (6 oz) drained canned black-eyed beans
90 g (3 oz) frozen peas or petits pois
1 tablespoon chopped fresh sage or 2 teaspoons
    dried sage
salt and freshly ground black pepper
4 tablespoons vegetarian Parmesan cheese,
    grated finely

❶ Heat the oil in a large frying-pan and fry the onion and garlic for about 3–4 minutes until softened, stirring frequently. Add the pepper and courgette, and fry for 2 minutes.

❷ Stir in the chilli, turmeric, and rice, and stir-fry for 2–3 minutes. Then add the stock, wine, tomatoes, and beans. Bring to the boil, then reduce the heat, cover, and simmer for 10 minutes.

❸ Stir in the peas, sage, and seasoning. Simmer for another 5 minutes or until the rice is tender. Serve immediately sprinkled with the cheese.

Cooks note: If the rice becomes dry when cooking, add some more stock or water.

Weight Watchers note: Omit the Parmesan cheese and save 1¹/₂ Points per serving!

Middle Eastern-Style Peppers

These peppers, filled with fresh minty rice, raisins and pine kernels, are a real treat!

Serves: 4
Preparation time: 35–40 minutes + 20 minutes
    cooking
Calories per serving: 425
Points per serving: 6¹/₂
Total Points per recipe: 26
Freezing: not recommended

4 orange peppers, de-seeded and cut in half
    lengthwise
1 tablespoon olive oil

1 onion, chopped finely
1 or 2 garlic cloves, crushed
240 g (8 oz) long-grain white rice
750 ml (1¹/₄ pints) vegetable stock
2 tomatoes, chopped
15 g (¹/₂ oz) pine nuts, toasted
45 g (1¹/₂ oz) raisins
3 tablespoons chopped fresh mint
¹/₂ teaspoon lemon juice
90 g (3 oz) vegetarian feta cheese, crumbled
salt and freshly ground black pepper

① Preheat the oven to Gas Mark 6/200°C/400°F.

② Place the pepper halves in a baking dish and bake in the oven for 20–25 minutes until softened.

③ Meanwhile, heat the oil in a large frying-pan and fry the onion and garlic gently for 5 minutes or until soft. Add the rice and stir well, cooking until the rice is browned all over. Stir in the stock, and tomatoes and cook for 15–20 minutes or until the rice is just tender and the stock has been absorbed.

④ Stir in the pine nuts, raisins, mint, and lemon juice and season to taste.

⑤ Spoon the rice mixture into the peppers and sprinkle over the feta cheese. Bake in the preheated oven for 20 minutes and serve immediately.

Cook's note: To toast the pine kernels, place in a grill pan and place under a moderate grill for a few minutes, stirring frequently until golden.

Chilli and Pepper Pasta

A great supper dish – quick to make, with a real kick to it!

Serves: 4
Preparation time: 15 minutes + 20 minutes cooking
Calories per serving: 390
Points per serving: 3¹/₂
Total Points per recipe: 14
Freezing: not recommended

240 g (8 oz) spaghetti, rigatoni, penne or conchiglie
60 g (2 oz) low-fat vegetarian Cheddar cheese, grated
For the sauce:
1 tablespoon olive oil

1 large onion, chopped finely
2 garlic cloves, crushed
1–2 large red chillis, de-seeded and chopped very finely
1 red pepper, de-seeded and chopped
2 yellow peppers, de-seeded and chopped
2 courgettes, chopped
420 g (14 oz) canned chopped tomatoes
210 g (7 oz) canned chopped tomatoes
2 tablespoons tomato purée
2 tablespoons shredded fresh basil
salt and freshly ground black pepper

① Heat the oil in a pan and fry the onion, garlic and chilli for 5 minutes until softened. Add the peppers, cover, and cook for 5 minutes, stirring occasionally. Add the courgettes and cook covered for a further 10 minutes.

② Add both cans of tomatoes and tomato purée, bring to the boil, and then reduce the heat and simmer gently for 20 minutes. Season to taste and stir in the basil.

③ Meanwhile, bring a large pan of salted water to the boil and cook the pasta for 10–12 minutes until *al dente*. Drain well.

④ Divide the pasta between 4 warm plates or bowls and top with the sauce. Sprinkle with the cheese and serve immediately.

Cook's note: If you wish, use the same amount of vegetarian Parmesan instead of vegetarian Cheddar. The Points will be 4¹/₂ per serving and 18 per recipe.

Mushroom Risotto Bake

This bake uses shiitake mushrooms which are a rich-flavoured wild mushroom widely used in Japanese cooking.
If you are unable to find them in the supermarket, use 120 g (4 oz) extra of the other mushrooms.
Together, the mushrooms and risotto rice make this bake wholesome and filling. Serve accompanied by
steamed green vegetables or a green salad.

Serves: 4

Preparation time: 20 minutes + 35–45 minutes
cooking

Calories per serving: 355

Points per serving: 5

Total Points per recipe: 20

Freezing: not recommended

4 teaspoons olive oil
1 onion, chopped finely
2 garlic cloves, crushed

180 g (6 oz) open-cup mushrooms, chopped
180 g (6 oz) button mushrooms, sliced
180 g (6 oz) chestnut or closed-cup mushrooms
120 g (4 oz) shiitake mushrooms, sliced
240 g (8 oz) risotto rice
750 ml (1½ pints) vegetable stock
1 teaspoon dried parsley
60 g (2 oz) low-fat vegetarian Cheddar cheese,
grated finely
15 g (½ oz) fresh white breadcrumbs
salt and freshly ground black pepper

❶ Preheat the oven to Gas Mark 6/200°C/400°F or the grill to a moderate heat.

❷ Heat the oil in a heavy-based flameproof casserole dish and fry the onion for 2 minutes. Add the garlic, mushrooms and seasoning and gently fry, stirring frequently for 10 minutes.

❸ Stir in the rice and add a ladle of stock. Cook until the liquid has been absorbed. Add another ladle of stock and cook until this has been absorbed.

Repeat this process until the rice is tender – this will take about 25–30 minutes. Remove from the heat.

❹ Stir in the parsley and ½ of the cheese and season to taste. Mix the remaining cheese with the breadcrumbs and sprinkle over the top.

❺ Bake in the oven for 10–12 minutes or until golden. Alternatively place under the grill for a few minutes until the topping is golden.

Chilli and Pepper Pasta
Mushroom Risotto Bake

Casseroles, Stews and Curries

Here is a wonderful selection of one-pot dishes. A variety of protein foods such as lentils, grains and pulses are added to lots of vegetables to make wholesome and filling meals. This is comfort food at its best!

Spicy Chick-Pea Stew

This stew is served with couscous, a staple in North African countries. Couscous is made of small pellets of semolina and is available precooked in the supermarkets so it is very easy to prepare – it simply needs to be soaked in boiling water. You could also serve this stew with rice if you prefer (which would reduce the Points per serving to 6) but it is no substitute for the light and fluffy texture of couscous.

Serves: 4
Preparation time: 20 minutes + 40 minutes cooking
Calories per serving: 575
Points per serving: 8
Total Points per recipe: 32
Freezing: recommended

1¹/₂ **tablespoons groundnut, sunflower or vegetable oil**
1 **large onion, chopped**
2 **garlic cloves, crushed**
1 **large carrot, chopped**
1 **teaspoon each of ground ginger, cinnamon and turmeric**

2 **teaspoons each of ground cumin and coriander**
1 **teaspoon chilli powder**
¹/₂ **small aubergine, chopped**
1 **courgette, chopped**
180 g (6 oz) **cauliflower florets**
4 **ripe tomatoes, peeled and chopped**
600 ml (1 pint) **vegetable stock**
420 g (14 oz) **canned chick-peas, rinsed and drained**
60 g (2 oz) **raisins**
2 **tablespoons chopped fresh coriander**
240 g (8 oz) **couscous**
salt and freshly ground black pepper

❶ Heat the oil in a large saucepan. Add the onion, garlic, and carrot. Cover and cook for 10 minutes, stirring occasionally, to prevent sticking.

❷ Stir in the spices, aubergine, courgette and cauliflower. Cook for 1 minute. Then add the tomatoes, stock, chick-peas, raisins and seasoning. Bring to the boil. Then reduce the heat, cover, and simmer gently for 40 minutes.

❸ Meanwhile, prepare the couscous according to the directions on the packet.

❹ Divide the couscous between 4 warmed plates or bowls and top with the stew. Sprinkle over the coriander and serve.

Parsnip and Prune Casserole

A simple, yet oh-so-tasty, casserole. Ideal for a midweek supper.

Serves: 4
Preparation and cooking time: 35–40 minutes
Calories per serving: 480
Points per serving: 7
Total Points per recipe: 28
Freezing: not recommended

4 teaspoons sunflower margarine
1 onion, chopped
1 leek, sliced
300 g (10 oz) parsnips, chopped

240 g (8 oz) carrots, sliced
240 g (8 oz) swede, chopped
30 g (1 oz) plain flour
150 ml (1/4 pint) dry cider
600 ml (1 pint) vegetable stock
2 bay leaves
120 g (4 oz) prunes
150 ml (5 fl oz) Greek yogurt
2 teaspoons chopped fresh sage
salt and freshly ground pepper
240 g (8 oz) cooked rice, to serve

1 Melt the margarine in a large saucepan. Add the onion and leek and cook until softened. Then add the root vegetables, cover, and cook for 10 minutes, stirring occasionally.

2 Stir in the flour and cook for 1 minute. Then stir in the cider and stock and slowly bring to the boil.

Stir in the bay leaves and prunes. Reduce the heat, and simmer for 15–20 minutes or until the vegetables are tender.

3 Remove from the heat and stir in the Greek yogurt and sage. Season to taste. Serve on a bed of cooked rice.

Winter Warmer Casserole

A rich and satisfying stew, ideal for those cold winter months. This stew is delicious served with mashed potato – but remember to add the necessary Points, with perhaps a brisk walk beforehand to earn a sprinkling of grated Cheddar cheese on the potato!

Serves: 4
Preparation and cooking time: 1 hour
Calories per serving: 235
Points per serving: 2 1/2
Total Points per recipe: 10
Freezing: recommended

120 g (4 oz) swede, diced
1 tablespoon sunflower margarine
1 onion, chopped roughly
2 garlic cloves, chopped
1 small leek, halved lengthways and sliced

120 g (4 oz) carrots, sliced
120 g (4 oz) turnip, diced
120 g (4 oz) celeriac or parsnip, diced
240 g (8 oz) potato, chopped
150 ml (1/4 pint) red wine
600 ml (1 pint) vegetable stock
60 g (2 oz) pearl barley
4 tomatoes, peeled and chopped
1 bay leaf
1 teaspoon dried mixed herbs
120 g (4 oz) baby button mushrooms, wiped
salt and freshly ground black pepper

1. Cook the swede in a pan of boiling water until tender, then drain and mash.

2. Heat the margarine in a large saucepan or flameproof casserole dish until melted and then add the onion. Cover and cook for 10 minutes, stirring occasionally. Add the garlic, leek, carrots, turnip, celeriac or parsnip, and potato. Cook covered for a further 5 minutes.

3. Add the red wine, stock, pearl barley, tomatoes and herbs to the fried vegetables. Bring to the boil, then cover, reduce the heat, and simmer for 15 minutes.

4. Stir in the mashed swede and mushrooms, season well and simmer for a further 20 minutes. Remove the bay leaf and serve.

Cauliflower and Potato Masala

Serves: 4
Preparation and cooking time: 40 minutes
Calories per serving: 375
Points per serving: 7^1/$_2$
Total Points per recipe: 30
Freezing: not recommended

2 teaspoons vegetable oil
1 teaspoon sunflower margarine
1 large onion, chopped
2 garlic cloves, crushed
5 cm (2-inch) piece of root ginger, grated finely

4 tablespoons mild curry paste
720 g (1^1/$_2$ lb) potatoes, chopped
360 g (12 oz) cauliflower florets
90 g (3 oz) red lentils
2 tomatoes, chopped
600 ml (1 pint) water
1 tablespoon garam masala
2 tablespoons mango chutney
4 tablespoons Greek yogurt
1 tablespoon lemon juice
1 tablespoon chopped fresh coriander
4 mini naan breads, to serve

1. Heat the oil and margarine in a pan and fry the onion, partially covered, for 10 minutes until softened and golden. Stir in the garlic, ginger, curry paste, potatoes and cauliflower. Fry for 2–3 minutes.

2. Add the lentils, tomatoes, and water. Bring to the boil, then reduce the heat, cover and simmer for 20 minutes. Preheat the grill to a medium heat. Warm the naan breads under a medium-hot grill for about five minutes. Meanwhile, stir the garam masala and mango chutney into the pan and cook for 1 minute. Then remove the pan from the heat and stir in the yogurt, lemon juice and coriander. Heat through without boiling and serve immediately with warm naan.

Variation: Try adding 30 g (1 oz) finely chopped spinach leaves with the mango chutney in step 2.

Mixed Vegetable and Bean Ragout

This ratatouille-style sauce is especially tasty with a tablespoon of pesto sauce.

Serves: 4

Preparation time: 35–40 minutes + 20 minutes cooking

Calories per serving: 285

Points per serving: 4

Total Points per recipe: 16

Freezing: recommended

1 tablespoon olive oil
1 large onion, chopped
1 garlic clove, peeled and crushed
1 small aubergine, diced
2 courgettes, diced
1 orange or yellow pepper, de-seeded and
    chopped

150 g (5 oz) mushrooms, quartered or sliced
150 ml (¼ pint) vegetable stock
6 tablespoons dry white wine
420 g (14 oz) canned chopped tomatoes
420 g (14 oz) canned cannellini beans, drained
    and rinsed
2 tablespoons tomato purée
2 tablespoons vegetarian pesto sauce
salt and freshly ground black pepper
For the garlic toasts:
120 g (4 oz) French baguette (½ thin baguette)
2 teaspoons sunflower margarine
1 tablespoon chopped fresh parsley
3–4 garlic cloves, crushed

❶ Preheat the oven to Gas Mark 6/200°C/400°F.

❷ Heat the oil in a flameproof casserole dish, and fry the onion until softened. Then add the garlic, aubergine, courgettes, pepper and mushrooms. Cover and cook for 15 minutes.

❸ Pour in the stock, wine, and tomatoes. Then stir in the beans, tomato purée and pesto sauce. Bring to the boil, then reduce the heat and simmer for 10–15 minutes.

❹ Meanwhile, slice the baguette on a slant into 8 thick slices. Melt the margarine, remove from the heat and stir in the parsley and crushed garlic. Brush the margarine mixture onto the bread slices.

❺ Remove the casserole from the heat and season to taste. Arrange the bread slices on top of the stew and cook in the oven, uncovered for 20 minutes or until the toasts are crisp and golden. Serve immediately.

Cook's note: Look out for vegetarian pesto sauce in the health food shop if you are a strict vegetarian, since the pesto sauce available from supermarkets normally contains non-vegetarian Parmesan cheese.

Gumbo Stew with Speedy Cornbread

Gumbo is a stew-like soup from New Orleans. Speedy and scrumptious cornbread buns are a refreshing change from rice and potatoes.

Serves: 4
Preparation and cooking time: 50–60 minutes
Calories per serving: 415
Points per serving: 6¹/₂
Total Points per recipe: 26
Freezing: not recommended

1 tablespoon sunflower oil
1 large onion, chopped finely
2 garlic cloves, crushed
1 large red chilli, de-seeded and chopped finely
1 red pepper, halved, de-seeded and chopped
1 yellow or orange pepper, halved, de-seeded
    and chopped
300 g (10 oz) sweet potato, chopped
180 g (6 oz) okra, trimmed
630 g (21 oz) canned chopped tomatoes
300 ml (¹/₂ pint) water

2 tablespoons light soy sauce
420 g (14 oz) canned black-eyed beans, drained
    and rinsed
180 g (6 oz) baby sweetcorn, chopped
2 bay leaves
2 teaspoons dried oregano or marjoram
1 teaspoon allspice
salt and freshly ground black pepper
For the cornbread:
60 g (2 oz) wholemeal flour
60 g (2 oz) cornmeal/polenta
¹/₂ tablespoon caster sugar
1¹/₄ teaspoons baking powder
¹/₂ teaspoon salt
¹/₂ tablespoon roasted cumin seeds
1 free-range egg
120 ml (4 fl oz) skimmed milk
1 tablespoon sunflower oil

❶ Preheat the oven to Gas Mark 6/200°C/400°F.
❷ Heat the oil and fry the onion, garlic and chilli for 10 minutes or until tender.
❸ Add the peppers, sweet potato and okra. Stir-fry for a couple of minutes. Then add the remaining ingredients, season, bring to the boil, and cover and simmer gently for 30–40 minutes, or until the vegetables are tender.
❹ Meanwhile, prepare the cornbread. Mix together the flour and polenta, sugar, baking powder, salt and cumin in a large bowl. Beat together the egg, milk and oil, and then quickly whisk this mixture into the

dry ingredients. Divide evenly between a muffin tin lined with 4 muffin cases. Bake for 10–15 minutes or until well risen and golden.
❺ Serve the gumbo with the cornbread.

Cook's note: To roast the cumin seeds, place them in a small non-stick heavy-based frying-pan and stir over a moderate heat until golden.

Variation: Serve the Gumbo topped with a tablespoon of low-fat plain yogurt. The Points will remain the same but Calories per serving will increase by 10.

Pies and Pizzas

Pastry and pizza are usually high on the list of foods to be avoided when you're watching your weight. But I think the worst thing you can do is to deprive yourself of foods you love – it only makes you want them more! So here is a chapter full of some of the things we all crave now and again – tailor-made to fit in with the Programme. These mouth-watering pies and pizzas have the Weight Watchers seal of approval, so enjoy!

Cheat's Mushroom and Courgette Pie

This is very quick to prepare – just top the creamy filling with a baked, ready-made puff pastry lid. Why not double the recipe and let someone else enjoy the pie too! Serve with steamed green vegetables.

Serves: 1
Preparation and cooking time: 20–25 minutes
Calories per serving: 355
Points per serving: 6
Total Points per recipe: 6
Freezing: not recommended

For the filling:
1 teaspoon sunflower margarine

3 small shallots, chopped finely
1 small courgette, diced
120 g (4 oz) mushrooms, sliced
45 g (1¹/₂ oz) garlic and herb low-fat soft cheese
2–3 tablespoons skimmed milk
salt and freshly ground black pepper
For the pastry:
45 g (1¹/₂ oz) puff pastry
1 teaspoon skimmed milk, to glaze

❶ Preheat the oven to Gas Mark 7/220°C/425°F.
❷ Heat the margarine in a saucepan and fry the shallots and courgette for 5 minutes until softened. Add the mushrooms and seasoning and cook gently for 5–8 minutes until tender.
❸ Meanwhile, roll out the pastry on a lightly floured surface, into a circle about 10 cm (4-inch) wide. Place on a dampened baking tray, lightly score a criss-cross pattern on the top with a knife and

brush with the milk. Bake for 5–8 minutes or until risen, crisp and golden.
❹ Add the cheese and 2 tablespoons of milk to the mushroom mixture. Stir over a gentle heat until melted, adding more milk if necessary to give a thick sauce consistency. Season to taste.
❺ Spoon the mushroom mixture on to a serving plate and top with the pastry lid.

Ciabatta Pizza
Cheat's Mushroom and Courgette Pie

Mediterranean Pizza

The thin scone base is easy to make and topped with a tasty assortment of Mediterranean flavours, it is well worth the effort! The results are absolutely scrumptious.

Serves: 4

Preparation Time: 30–35 minutes + 20 minutes cooking

Calories per serving: 355

Points per serving: 7

Total Points per recipe: 28

Freezing: not recommended

1 small aubergine, sliced into 1 cm (¹/₂-inch) slices

For the base:
180 g (6 oz) self-raising flour
¹/₂ teaspoon salt
3 tablespoons sunflower margarine
90–120 ml (3–4 fl oz) skimmed milk
1 tablespoon flour, for rolling

For the tomato sauce:
150 ml (¹/₄ pint) passata

2 garlic cloves, crushed
1 tablespoon sun-dried tomato purée
1 tablespoon shredded fresh basil
salt and freshly ground black pepper

For the topping:
2 plum tomatoes, cut into segments
1 pepper, de-seeded and chopped
2 spring onions, sliced thinly
120 g (4 oz) frozen chopped spinach, thawed and drained well
45 g (1¹/₂ oz) vegetarian feta cheese, crumbled
15 g (¹/₂ oz) low-fat vegetarian Cheddar cheese, grated finely
60 g (2 oz) vegetarian mozzarella cheese, sliced thinly
8 pitted black olives
1 tablespoon chopped fresh parsley

1 Preheat the oven to Gas Mark 7/220°C/425°F.

2 Place the aubergine slices on a greased baking tray and bake in the oven for 15 minutes until golden and tender.

3 To make the base, sift the flour and salt together in a bowl and then rub in the margarine. Using a blunt-ended knife, stir in enough milk to give a soft but not sticky dough.

4 Roll the dough out on a lightly-floured surface to a 30 cm (12-inch) round, and place it on a baking sheet lined with parchment paper.

5 Mix together all the tomato sauce ingredients and then spread over the base. Arrange the baked aubergine slices, tomato, pepper and spring onion on top.

6 With your hands, squeeze out any excess liquid from the spinach. Arrange small mounds of the spinach mixture onto the pizza.

7 Finally, scatter the cheeses and the olives on top. Bake for 20 minutes in the oven. Sprinkle over the parsley and serve immediately.

Weight Watchers note: Passata is simply a smooth purée of tomatoes and is available from the supermarket either in jars or cartons. It can be found beside the canned tomatoes and tomato purées. You can also use low-fat vegetarian Parmesan cheese instead of the Cheddar. This will add 2¹/₂ Points per serving.

Speedy Spinach and Feta Pie

This is a version of the Greek traditional dish 'Spanakopitta'. Spinach and crumbled feta in a crisp filo pastry case is a favourite in Greece and may become one of yours too!

Serves: 4

Preparation and cooking time: 20 minutes + 20 minutes cooking

Calories per serving: 420

Points per serving: 9

Total Points per recipe: 36

Freezing: not recommended

For the filling:
960 g (2 lb) young spinach leaves, rinsed and drained

8 spring onions, chopped
240 g (8 oz) vegetarian feta cheese
1 free-range egg, beaten
a good pinch of grated nutmeg
1 tablespoon chopped fresh mint
freshly ground black pepper
For the pastry casing:
8 × 23 cm × 23 cm (9-inch × 9-inch) filo pastry sheets (180 g/6 oz), defrosted before use if frozen
6 teaspoons sunflower margarine, melted

❶ Preheat the oven to Gas Mark 5/190°C/375°F.

❷ Place the spinach in a large saucepan, cover and cook over a gentle heat for a few minutes, until the leaves are cooked and wilted. Remove from the heat, tip into a sieve and leave to drain and cool.

❸ Using a wooden spoon, rub the spinach in the sieve to remove as much moisture as possible. Then finely chop the spinach and place in a bowl. Mix in the spring onions. Roughly crumble in the feta cheese and then add the remaining filling ingredients. Stir to combine.

❹ Brush 3 of the filo pastry sheets with some of the margarine, and place them on top of one another, on a greased baking sheet. Spoon over the spinach mixture leaving a 2.5 cm (1-inch) border. Level the surface of the mixture with the back of a spoon, then fold the pastry border over the edges of the filling.

❺ Cut the remaining pastry sheets in half, brush with ⅓ of the margarine and use 6 halves to encase the filling by overlapping them. Loosely scrunch up the remaining 4 halves of pastry and arrange on top of the pie, for decoration.

❻ Brush the pie with any remaining margarine and bake in the oven for 20 minutes or until crisp and golden.

Cook's note: When the filo sheets are not in use, cover them with a damp tea towel to prevent them from drying out and cracking. Any left-over sheets can be stored in the freezer.

Tomato, Mozzarella and Garlic Tart

This is a must for garlic lovers! Delicious simply served with a mixed salad. Serve hot or cold.

Serves: 4

Preparation time: 30 minutes + 45 minutes
chilling + 20–25 minutes cooking

Calories per serving: 355

Points per serving: 6½

Total Points per recipe: 26

Freezing: not recommended

For the pastry:
120 g (4 oz) plain flour
a pinch of salt
60 g (2 oz) block margarine (i.e. not soft)
3–4 tablespoons ice-cold water
For the filling:
**480 g (1 lb) fresh tomatoes, peeled and chopped
roughly**

2 teaspoons olive oil
1 tablespoon tomato purée
2 garlic cloves, peeled and chopped
a pinch of sugar
2 tablespoons shredded fresh basil leaves
1 teaspoon dried oregano
1 free-range egg, beaten
5 tablespoons skimmed milk
**60 g (2 oz) vegetarian mozzarella cheese,
chopped**
**30 g (1 oz) low-fat vegetarian Cheddar cheese,
grated**
salt and freshly ground black pepper

1 Preheat the oven to Gas Mark 6/200°C/400°F.

2 To make the pastry, sift the flour and salt into a bowl and rub in the margarine, using your fingertips, until the mixture resembles fine breadcrumbs. With a blunt-ended knife, stir in enough water to form a soft but not sticky dough. Knead the dough gently until smooth, then wrap in a plastic bag and chill for 30 minutes in the fridge.

3 Roll out the chilled pastry on a lightly floured surface and use to line a 19 cm (7½-inch) round flan tin. Chill for 15 minutes, then prick the base with a fork and line the case with aluminium foil, or baking parchment, and baking beans. Bake the pastry for 10 minutes or until it is just set. Then lift out the foil, or baking parchment, and beans and bake for another 5 minutes.

4 Meanwhile, place the tomatoes in a saucepan with the olive oil, tomato purée, 1 garlic clove, a pinch of sugar and seasoning. Cook over a moderate heat until bubbling, then lower the heat and gently simmer, partially covered, for 10 minutes or until the tomato sauce is thick and pulpy. Remove from the heat, stir in the remaining garlic clove, basil and oregano and allow to cool.

5 Beat together the egg and milk and then stir into the tomato sauce. Spread half over the pastry case. Arrange half the mozzarella cheese on top and sprinkle over half the grated Cheddar cheese. Repeat the layers once with the remaining ingredients.

6 Bake in the oven for 20–25 minutes or until set and golden.

Ciabatta Pizzas

These easy-as-pie pizzas are the ideal snack. There are two yummy toppings to choose from.

Serves: 1

Preparation and cooking time: 12–20 minutes

Calories per serving: 320

Points per serving: with the mozzarella, tomato and pesto topping 9¹/₂; with the garlic mushroom topping 8¹/₂

Freezing: not recommended

For the base:

90 g (3 oz) piece ciabatta bread or roll, halved crossways

For the mozzarella, tomato and pesto topping:

1 tablespoon vegetarian pesto sauce

1 tablespoon tomato purée

1 large tomato, sliced

30 g (1 oz) vegetarian mozzarella cheese, sliced

For the garlic mushroom topping:

2 tablespoons passata

¹/₂ tablespoon tomato purée

1 teaspoon vegetable oil

¹/₄ small onion, chopped finely

1 small garlic clove, crushed

120 g (4 oz) baby button mushrooms, sliced

15 g (¹/₂ oz) garlic and herb low-fat soft cheese

15 g (¹/₂ oz) low-fat vegetarian Cheddar cheese, grated finely

❶ Preheat the grill. Toast the cut side of the bread until golden. Remove from the heat leaving the grill on.

❷ For the mozzarella, tomato and pesto pizza: Mix together the pesto and tomato purée and spread over the toasted sides of the bread. Top with the sliced tomato and then the mozzarella cheese.

For the garlic mushroom pizza: Mix together the passata and tomato purée and spread over the toasted sides of the bread. Heat the oil in a small saucepan and fry the onion until softened. Add the garlic and mushrooms and cook for 4 minutes or until softened. Spread over the pizza base. Top with dabs of garlic cheese and finally sprinkle over the Cheddar.

❸ Place the pizzas under the grill for 5 minutes or until they are heated through and the cheese has melted.

Spicy Samosas

Spice up your life with these tasty little parcels without putting on the pounds!

Serves: 4

Preparation time: 25–30 minutes + 20 minutes
 cooking

Calories per serving: 460

Points per serving: 9

Total Points per recipe: 36

Freezing: not recommended

2 teaspoons vegetable oil

1 onion, chopped finely

2 carrots, diced finely

1 garlic clove, crushed

120 g (4 oz) mushrooms, diced finely

2.5 cm (1-inch) piece root ginger, grated

1 teaspoon ground cumin

1 teaspoon ground coriander

1 teaspoon ground turmeric

240 g (8 oz) potato, cooked and diced finely

210 g (7 oz) canned aduki beans, drained

1 tablespoon tomato purée

100 ml (3¹/₂ fl oz) water

45 g (1¹/₂ oz) petit pois

For the pastry:

12 × 25 cm (10-inch) square sheets filo pastry
 (270 g/9 oz)

8 teaspoons sunflower margarine, melted

1 teaspoon sesame seeds

For the minted yogurt dip:

300 ml (¹/₂ pint) plain bio-yogurt

¹/₂ teaspoon ground cumin (optional)

2 tablespoons chopped fresh mint

1 Preheat the oven to Gas Mark 6/200°C/400°F.

2 Heat the oil in a saucepan and fry the onion and carrots until tender and lightly browned. Then add the garlic, mushrooms, ginger and spices. Continue to cook for 3–4 minutes.

3 Stir in the potato, beans, tomato purée, water, and peas. Gently simmer, until the mixture is thick and fairly dry. Allow to cool.

4 Brush the filo pastry sheets with some of the melted margarine and fold in half. Brush again with the margarine. Place a tablespoon of the cooled filling at one end of each strip and fold the corner of the pastry over the filling to form a triangle. Turn the

triangle over and over to overwrap to the end of the pastry.

5 Place the triangles on a greased baking tray and brush with the remaining melted margarine. Sprinkle over the sesame seeds and bake for 10 minutes or until crisp and golden.

6 Meanwhile, mix together all the dip ingredients and spoon into a serving dish. Eat the samosas hot or cold accompanied by the dip.

Cook's note: If you don't have all the spices, you could substitute 2 tablespoons of curry powder.

Grills, Roasts and Bakes

As these recipes prove, vegetarian food is a whole lot more than a plate of vegetables! Here you'll find a wide variety of flavours, textures and cooking methods which show just how exciting and tasty modern vegetarian cuisine can be. If you think tofu is bland, you'll get a surprise when you taste the Curried Tofu Burgers. All these recipes have been carefully planned to fit into the Weight Watchers Programme. Enjoy the food, lose weight and feel great. It's that simple!

Stuffed and Roasted Aubergines

The fine grains of minced Quorn make a tasty, textured sauce.

Serves: 4
Preparation time: 30 minutes + 15 minutes cooking
Calories per serving: 120
Points per serving: 2
Total Points per recipe: 8
Freezing: recommended

2 large aubergines
2 teaspoons olive oil
1 small onion, chopped
90 g (3 oz) minced Quorn
2 garlic cloves, chopped finely
120 g (4 oz) open-cup mushrooms, chopped
420 g (14 oz) canned chopped tomatoes
$^1/_2$ teaspoon hot chilli powder
2 tablespoons tomato purée
$^1/_2$ tablespoon chopped fresh parsley
salt and freshly ground black pepper
For the topping:
15 g ($^1/_2$ oz) fresh white breadcrumbs
15 g ($^1/_2$ oz) finely grated vegetarian Parmesan cheese

1 Preheat the oven to Gas Mark 6/200°C/400°F.

2 Bring a large pan of water to the boil. Prick the aubergines and boil for about 10 minutes until softened. Remove from the pan and allow to cool.

3 Meanwhile, heat the oil and gently fry the onion for 5 minutes until softened.

4 Place the Quorn in a food processor and blend until finely chopped. Set aside.

5 Cut the aubergines in half lengthwise and scoop out the aubergine flesh, leaving a 1 cm ($^1/_2$-inch)

border around the edge. Chop up the aubergine flesh and add to the onions with the garlic, mushrooms and Quorn. Continue to cook for 5 minutes.

6 Stir in the tomatoes, chilli powder, and tomato purée. Bring to the boil and simmer for 5 minutes. Stir in the parsley and seasoning.

7 Spoon the mixture into the aubergine halves and place in a baking tin or shallow ovenproof dish. Sprinkle over the breadcrumbs and cheese. Bake in the oven for 15 minutes or until golden.

Roasted Vegetables with Speedy Houmous

These roasted vegetables, coated with an olive oil, garlic and herb mixture, and served with a chick-pea sauce are an ideal starter or light meal.

Serves: 4

Preparation time: 20 minutes + 20 minutes cooking

Calories per serving: 550

Points per serving: with houmous 8½;
without houmous 5

Total Points per recipe: with houmous 34;
without houmous 20

Freezing: not recommended

8 teaspoons olive oil

2 garlic cloves, chopped very finely

a sprig of rosemary or thyme

240 g (8 oz) cooked baby new potatoes, halved
or quartered

1 red onion, cut into wedges

150 g (5 oz) baby sweetcorn

2 red peppers, halved, de-seeded and cut into
thick strips

1 yellow or orange pepper, halved, de-seeded and
cut into thick strips

2 large courgettes, cut into thick strips

120 g (4 oz) small open-cup mushrooms

4 medium-size pitta breads, warmed, to serve

For the houmous:

420 g (14 oz) canned chick-peas, rinsed and
drained

180 ml (6 fl oz) water

6 tablespoons lemon juice

4 tablespoons tahini

3 garlic cloves, crushed

¼ teaspoon paprika

salt and freshly ground black pepper

❶ Preheat the oven to Gas Mark 7/220°C/425°F.

❷ In a large bowl, mix together the oil and garlic. Remove the leaves of the rosemary or thyme from the stems and add to the oil mixture with plenty of seasoning. Add all the vegetables and toss to coat. Tip into a large baking tin and bake in the oven for 20 minutes or until charred and tender.

❸ Place the chick-peas in a saucepan with the water and bring to the boil. Remove from the heat and cool slightly. Place in a food processor or blender and process thoroughly. Then add the remaining ingredients and process to give a smooth sauce. Transfer into a serving dish.

❹ Place the pitta breads in the oven for a few minutes to warm through, then split open and fill with the vegetables and drizzle over the houmous sauce.

Cook's note: For a lighter snack, you can serve these roasted vegetables with a minted yogurt sauce instead of the houmous. Simply mix 2 tablespoons of chopped fresh mint leaves with 10 fl oz of low-fat bio-yogurt. The Points per serving will be 5½.

The cooked vegetables could also be served on a bed of cooked bulgar wheat, couscous or rice (the Points per serving respectively will be 7, 8 and 8½) instead of pitta bread. Simply use 240 g (8 oz) of any of these rices and cook according to the directions on the packet.

Roasted Vegetables with Speedy Houmous
Potato Layer Bake

Potato Layer Bake

If you love potatoes, this one's for you!

Serves: 4

Preparation time: 30 minutes + 50–60 minutes cooking

Calories per serving: 415

Points per serving: 6½

Total Points per recipe: 26

Freezing: not recommended

960 g (2 lb) waxy potatoes, peeled
1 red pepper
1 yellow pepper
1 teaspoon vegetarian pesto sauce
1 tablespoon olive oil

1 large onion, chopped
2 garlic cloves, crushed
240 g (8 oz) closed-cup mushrooms, sliced
1 teaspoon dried oregano
210 g (7 oz) canned chopped tomatoes
1 tablespoon tomato purée
1 tablespoon shredded fresh basil leaves
120 g (4 oz) vegetarian mozzarella cheese, quartered and sliced thinly
30 g (1 oz) low-fat vegetarian Cheddar cheese, grated
salt and freshly ground black pepper

❶ Preheat the oven to Gas Mark 6/200°C/400°F.

❷ Cook the potatoes in a pan of boiling salted water until they are tender but not falling apart. Tip into a colander, refresh under running cold water and then leave to cool.

❸ Place the peppers on a baking tray and bake in the oven for about 15 minutes until the skins are charred. Remove from the oven, cover with a tea towel and leave to cool. Once cooled, peel off the skins, de-seed and chop. Place in a bowl and mix in the pesto sauce. Turn the oven down to Gas Mark 4/180°C/350°F.

❹ Heat the oil in a frying-pan and fry the onion until softened. Stir in the garlic and cook for 1 minute. Remove half the onion mixture and reserve. Add the mushrooms to the remaining half of the mixture in the pan, season well, and stir-fry for a few minutes until tender. Remove from the heat and stir in the oregano.

❺ Place the reserved onions in a food processor or blender. Add the canned tomatoes and tomato purée and process to give a smooth sauce. Pour the sauce into a small pan and simmer gently for about 5 minutes until very thick. Remove from the heat and stir in the basil.

❻ Thinly slice the potatoes and arrange ⅓ of them in the base of a shallow ovenproof baking dish. Spread over half the tomato sauce and top with half the mushrooms and peppers. Scatter over ⅓ of the mozzarella and Cheddar. Repeat the layers finishing with potatoes and then the remaining cheese.

❼ Bake in the oven for 50–60 minutes or until tender and golden.

Cook's note: The potatoes are easier to slice if they are cooked, cooled and chilled in the fridge. It's a great way of using up any leftover boiled potatoes.

Curried Tofu Burgers

Tofu is made from soya bean which is high in protein and low in fat and is so versatile because it absorbs the flavour of any sauce or spices it is blended with. Try to buy the chilled tofu, especially if you are using it cubed in casseroles or stir-fries; the vacuum-pack tofu tends to fall apart.

Makes: 4

Preparation time: 15 minutes + 30 minutes chilling + 10 minutes cooking

Calories per burger: 160

Points per burger: 1½

Total Points per recipe: 6

Freezing: not recommended

2 teaspoons sunflower oil
1 onion, grated finely

1 garlic clove, crushed
½ teaspoon hot chilli powder
1 teaspoon ground cumin
½ teaspoon ground coriander
½ teaspoon turmeric
2 teaspoons tomato purée
180 g (6 oz) chilled firm tofu
60 g (2 oz) brown rice, cooked
45 g (1½ oz) fresh wholemeal breadcrumbs

❶ Heat the oil in a large frying-pan and fry the onion for 4 minutes until softened. Add the garlic, spices, and tomato purée. Cook for 2 minutes. Remove from the heat.

❷ Place the tofu, and spicy onion mixture in a food processor or blender and process until smooth. Transfer to a bowl and stir in the rice and breadcrumbs.

❸ Divide the mixture into 4 equal portions and shape into burgers. Place on a plate lined with parchment paper and chill for ½ hour. Preheat the grill to a moderate heat five minutes before the chilling has finished.

❹ Place the burgers under the grill for 4–5 minutes on each side until golden.

Weight Watchers note: Try serving these burgers with these delicious low-fat chips. Preheat the oven to Gas Mark 7/220°C/425°F. Simply peel 960 g (2 lb) old potatoes and cut into strips. Dry the potato strips thoroughly on kitchen paper, then place them in a plastic container with 2 teaspoons sunflower oil. Put the lid on and shake vigorously. Spread the chips on a baking sheet lined with baking parchment and bake for 25–30 minutes until golden and crisp. Points per serving for the chips will be 3 and the Calories per serving will be 225.

Shepherdess Pie

This 'shepherd's' pie is rich and comforting, something the whole family will enjoy during the winter months.

Serves: 4
Preparation time: 1 hour
Cooking time: 15–20 minutes
Calories per serving: 435
Points per serving: 5
Total Points per recipe: 20
Freezing: recommended

2 teaspoons sunflower oil
1 leek, chopped finely
1 small courgette, diced
1 carrot, diced
1 garlic clove, crushed
120 g (4 oz) mushrooms, sliced
60 g (2 oz) red lentils

60 g (2 oz) green lentils
210 g (7 oz) canned chopped tomatoes
450 ml (³/₄ pint) water
1 bay leaf
¹/₂ teaspoon dried marjoram
¹/₂ teaspoon dried thyme
1¹/₂ tablespoons brown sauce
210 g (7 oz) canned baked beans
salt and freshly ground black pepper
For the topping:
960 g (2 lb) potatoes
5–6 tablespoons skimmed milk
30 g (1 oz) low-fat vegetarian Cheddar cheese,
    grated

❶ Preheat the oven to Gas Mark 6/200°C/400°F.

❷ Heat the oil and gently fry the leek, courgette, carrot, garlic and mushrooms for 10 minutes, covered, until soft.

❸ Add the lentils, tomatoes, water, and herbs, and bring the mixture to the boil. Then reduce the heat, partially cover, and simmer for 30 minutes or until the lentils are soft and the mixture is thick. Stir in the brown sauce and baked beans and cook for a further 5 minutes.

❹ Meanwhile, place the potatoes in a pan of salted water, bring to the boil and simmer for about 20 minutes until tender. Drain the potatoes, return to the pan and heat gently to dry out. Add the milk and seasoning and mash until smooth.

❺ Remove the bay leaf from the lentil mixture and spoon into a large ovenproof dish. Pile the potato on top and fork over. Sprinkle over the grated cheese.

❻ Bake in the oven for 15–20 minutes or until the potato is crispy. Serve immediately.

Tortilla Treat

This is a treat to share with friends or family: you can prepare everything in advance and then grill the dish in minutes.

Serves: 4

Preparation and cooking time: 30–35 minutes

Calories per serving: 340

Points per serving: 6

Total Points per recipe: 24

Freezing: not recommended

180 g (6 oz) tortilla chips or nachos

For the sauce:

1 teaspoon olive oil

¹/₂ small onion, chopped finely

1 chilli, de-seeded and chopped finely

1 garlic clove, crushed

420 g (14 oz) canned chopped tomatoes

2 tablespoons tomato purée

salt and freshly ground black pepper

For the topping:

4 tomatoes, chopped

1 pepper, de-seeded and diced

3 spring onions, chopped

1 large red chilli, de-seeded and chopped finely

1 tablespoon chopped fresh coriander

3 tablespoons Greek yogurt

60 g (2 oz) low-fat vegetarian Cheddar cheese, grated

❶ Preheat the grill to a moderate heat.

❷ To make the sauce, heat the oil and fry the onion for a few minutes until softened. Then add the chilli and garlic and cook for 1 minute. Stir in the canned tomatoes, tomato purée and seasoning. Remove from the heat and blend together in a food processor or blender until smooth. Return the sauce to the pan, bring to the boil and then simmer for 10–15 minutes or until very thick.

❸ Arrange the chips around the base and the sides of a flameproof shallow serving dish. Spoon the tomato sauce into the centre.

❹ To make the topping, mix together the tomatoes, pepper, spring onions, chilli and coriander. Spoon over the sauce. Place under the grill for a couple of minutes to heat the filling.

❺ Then spread over the Greek yogurt and sprinkle over the cheese. Put back under the grill until the cheese is melted and bubbling.

Index